Charlie

Kayla

Misty

Ella

Molly

Leroy

This annual belongs to...

Name:

Emily

X ♡

rachaelhale

ANNUAL 2011

igloo

Brooke

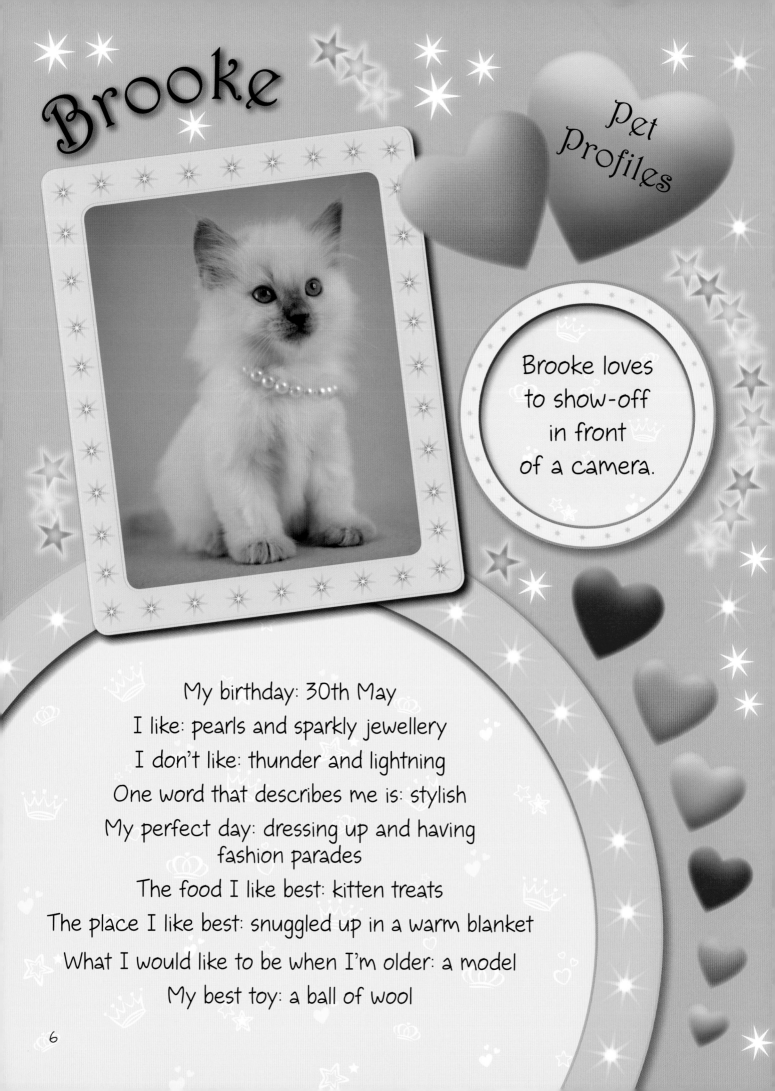

Brooke loves to show-off in front of a camera.

My birthday: 30th May

I like: pearls and sparkly jewellery

I don't like: thunder and lightning

One word that describes me is: stylish

My perfect day: dressing up and having fashion parades

The food I like best: kitten treats

The place I like best: snuggled up in a warm blanket

What I would like to be when I'm older: a model

My best toy: a ball of wool

Sophie

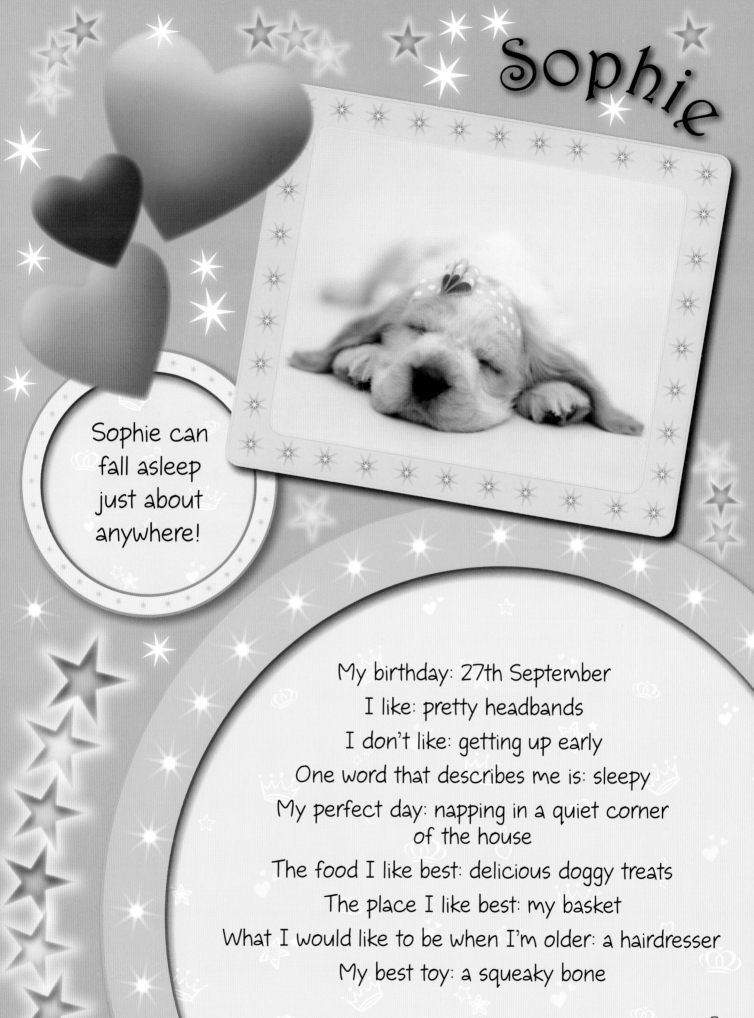

Sophie can fall asleep just about anywhere!

My birthday: 27th September

I like: pretty headbands

I don't like: getting up early

One word that describes me is: sleepy

My perfect day: napping in a quiet corner of the house

The food I like best: delicious doggy treats

The place I like best: my basket

What I would like to be when I'm older: a hairdresser

My best toy: a squeaky bone

Kitten Hide-and-Seek

Jimmy and Simba are playing a game of hide-and-seek.

Storytime

Jimmy

"I'm looking for Simba," says Jimmy, "but I can't find her anywhere. I'll ask Peaches if she has seen her."

"I've been packing all day for a trip and I haven't seen Simba," says Peaches. "Perhaps you should ask Kokomo?

Peaches

8

"Sorry, but she's not under this warm fluffy blanket with me," says Kokomo. "Have you asked Minnie if she has seen Simba?"

Kokomo

Minnie

"I've been in my hammock all day and I haven't seen her," says Minnie. "Toby might know where Simba is."

9

Toby

"Sorry, I've been busy painting and I haven't seen anyone," says Toby. "Maybe Hannah knows where she is?"

Hannah

"I've been outside chasing butterflies amongst the flowers," says Hannah. "Have you tried asking Guiness and Fatboy if they have seen Simba?"

Guiness and Fatboy

"Sorry, we've been sleeping all morning," say Guiness and Fatboy.

"I can't find Simba anywhere," says Jimmy.

Where could Simba be hiding?

Simba

"Here I am!" laughs Simba. "I was hiding in this pretty pink box the whole time. Now it's your turn to hide, Jimmy!" she laughs.

Spot the Difference

Zoe, Zola and Zeek love playing with boxes. Can you spot the five differences between the two pictures?

a

b

Close Up

Draw lines to match the close-up pieces to the pictures.

a

b

c

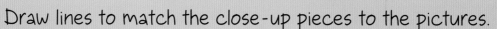

1

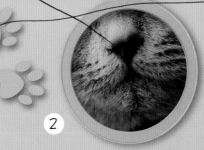

2

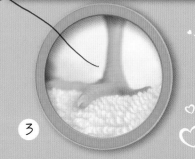

3

Odd One Out

Which of these animals is the odd one out?
What is different about it?

a

b

c

d

C

Silhouette Match

Which of these is the silhouette of Maddie?

Maddie

a

b

c

d

Answers on page 69

Playtime in the Park

You will need a friend to play with.
Each of you will need to use a coin for a counter.
You will also need a dice.

Game

Start

1

2

3
Chase a kite.
Move forward
two spaces.

4

13
Go for a swim
in the pond.
Move back a space.

14

12

15

16 Chase a ball. Move
forward two spaces.

17

18

19
Stop to have
a rest.
Miss a turn.

20

21

1. Each player chooses a sticker from the sticker sheet and sticks it to a coin. Put your coins on the start space.
2. Take turns to roll the dice.
3. Follow the instructions on the spaces where you land.
4. The first person to reach the puppies wins!

5

6

7 Stop to play in the leaves. Miss a turn.

8

9 Chase a butterfly. Move forward three spaces.

11

10

23 Stop to smell the flowers. Move back one space.

24

25

22

Finish

Bookmark

White card
Pink card
Pens
Glitter
Glue
Scissors

Aristotle

1. Ask an adult to cut out a strip of pink card 25cm (10 inches) long and 5cm (2 inches) wide.

2. Create patterns with the glue on the pink strip of card and sprinkle with glitter. Leave to dry.

3. When dry, shake off the excess glitter.

4. Then, draw any animal you like on the piece of white card. You could draw a cat, dog, or even a pony.

5. Once you have drawn your animal, ask an adult to cut it out for you. Decorate it any way you like, using your pens.

6. Glue your animal to one end of the long strip of card.

7. Now use your homemade bookmark in your annual!

Sock Puppet Puppy

Byron

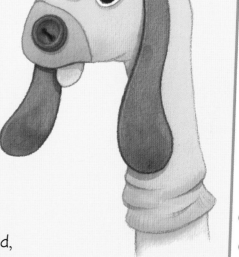

You will need:

An old sock
Brown felt
White paper
Pink felt
A button
A black pen
Scissors
Glue

1. Use an old sock for the body of your puppy. Ask an adult to cut two long ovals from the piece of brown felt and then glue them to either side of the sock, for ears.

2. Cut two small ovals from the white paper and draw a black circle on each. Glue these to the front of your sock for eyes.

3. Cut an oval from the pink felt and glue this on the sock for a tongue.

4. Finally, glue the button on the sock for the nose.

5. Try creating some other sock puppet animals.

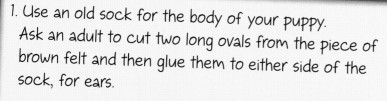

Top Tip! If you ask an adult to put the sock on their hand, you will find it easier to glue the ears, eyes, nose and tongue in the right places.

Quiz Whizz!

Piper

Missy

Indira

1. What do dogs like as a treat?
   a.   A fish
   b.   A bone
   c.   A carrot   *b*

2. Which of these animals can fly?
   a.   A butterfly
   b.   A bear
   c.   A guinea pig   *A*

3. Which animal is the fastest?
   a.   A snail
   b.   A mouse
   c.   A cheetah   *C*

4. Which animal would you find on a farm?
   a.   A giraffe
   b.   A pig
   c.   A zebra   *b*

5. Which of these animals does not have stripes?
   a.   A tiger
   b.   A leopard
   c.   A zebra   *b*

6. What type of animal is an emu?
   a.   A cat
   b.   A bird
   c.   A rabbit   *b*

Answers on page 69

18

Remember Me

Study this picture for twenty seconds, then cover it up and try and answer the questions on the following page.

Counting Fun

Each of these groups of animals can be added to another group to make 7 animals. Can you see which groups should be added together?

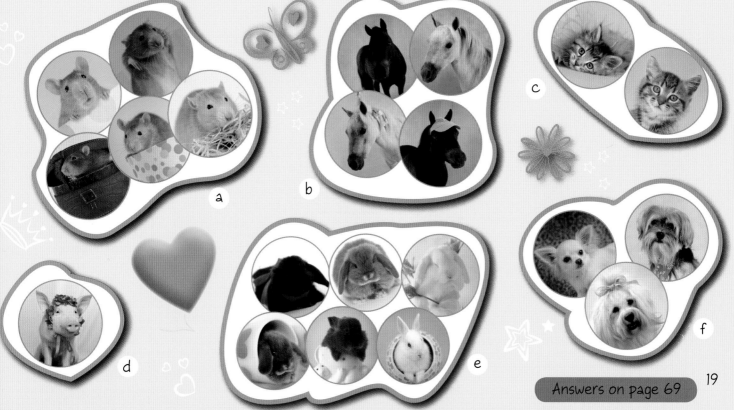

a

b

c

d

e

f

Answers on page 69

Who Eats What?

Draw lines to match up the animals
with what they like to eat.

Remember Me

Can you answer these questions from the picture on the previous page?
Write your answers in the white boxes.

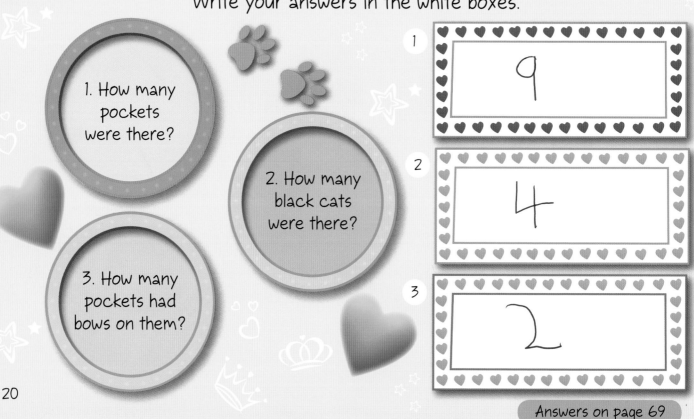

1. How many pockets were there?

2. How many black cats were there?

3. How many pockets had bows on them?

1 9

2 4

3 2

20

Answers on page 69

Missing Pieces

Each picture is missing something.
Can you match the missing pieces to the pictures?

1

2

3

a

b

c

Which Way?

Which line leads Malaika and Malai to their warm basket?

Finish

Start

a b c

21

Answers on page 69

Mopsy

Mopsy is so cute and fluffy and loves to play hide-and-seek.

My birthday: 2nd October

I like: bouncing in the garden

I don't like: getting up early

One word that describes me is: fluffy

My perfect day: playing in the sunshine

The food I like best: crunchy carrots

The place I like best: the garden shed

What I would like to be when I'm older:
a champion hopper

My best toy: a teddy bear

Ella

Ella likes to nibble and chew everything!

My birthday: 28th January

I like: pretty flowers

I don't like: bumblebees

One word that describes me is: quiet

My perfect day: going to the park

The food I like best: long, green grass

The place I like best: flowerbeds

What I would like to be when I'm older: a ballerina

My best toy: a rag doll

Puppy Playtime

It's a rainy day and everyone is keeping dry inside, but Molly wants to play a game.

Molly

"I wonder if anybody would like to play inside with me?" says Molly. "I think I'll ask Jesse."

"Sorry, but I'm too sleepy," says Jesse. "I'm just about to have my morning nap. Have you asked Maggie and Caesar?"

Jesse

"We're too busy
having a bubble bath,"
say Maggie and Caesar.
"Perhaps Ethan and Emma
would like to play?"

Maggie and Caesar

Ethan and Emma

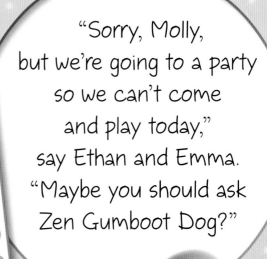

"Sorry, Molly,
but we're going to a party
so we can't come
and play today,"
say Ethan and Emma.
"Maybe you should ask
Zen Gumboot Dog?"

Zen Gumboot Dog

"I like the rain,"
says Zen Gumboot Dog.
"So I'm going to go for
a walk. I like jumping in
the puddles best.
Maybe Dickens will
play with you?"

Dickens

"Sorry, but I'm busy
reading a story book,"
says Dickens.
"Have you tried asking
Charlie? Perhaps he
would like to play?"

Charlie

"Sorry, Molly, but I have to tidy my toys away this morning," says Charlie. "But I might be able to play with you later."

Molly was sad, she couldn't find anyone to play with.

"We'll play with you!" bark Buffy and Biskit.

"We love games!" laughs Beau.

"Let's all play tag together!" they shout.

Buffy, Biskit and Beau

Bunny Card

You will need:
A piece of card
Crayons
Scissors
A Pencil
Glitter and sequins (optional)
Glue (optional)

Sage

1. Fold your piece of card in half. Then unfold it so it lies flat.

2. Draw a bunny on the piece of card so that the top is drawn over the fold, as shown in picture a.

3. Ask an adult to cut around the top half of your animal, but not across the center fold.

a

4. Now fold your card in half again and push the top half of your animal up, so it stands above the center fold, as shown in picture b.

b

5. You can decorate the card using your crayons. You could even add glitter, or sequins.

6. Try making all sorts of different animal cards.

Kitten Mask

You will need:

White card
Scissors
Tracing paper
Pens or crayons
Elastic (approx.
30cm/11 inches)
Glue

1. Trace the mask below onto some card.
2. Ask an adult to cut it out and to make holes below the ear on either side, for the elastic.
3. Decorate your mask with your crayons and pens.
4. Tie one end of the elastic to one of the holes on the side of the mask.
5. Hold the mask up to your face and ask an adult to tie the other end of the elastic through the other hole.
6. Now you're all ready to pretend you're a cat. Why not try making other animal masks?

Did you know...

Hummingbirds are the only birds that can fly backwards.

Penguins huddle in large groups of up to 5000 to stay warm in the Arctic.

Camels have three eye lids.

A zebra is black with white stripes.

Most people believe giraffes have no vocal chords. They do, they just don't use them.

In some countries, people eat fried bugs – yuck!

Ducks have waterproof feathers.

Mayflies only live for one day.

Bees should not be able to fly because their bodies are too big for their wings.

Parrots can mimic humans. They can make other sounds as well.

Koalas rarely drink anything. They can get all of their liquids from the Eucalyptus leaves they eat.

A giraffe has a black tongue.

The Blue Whale is the largest animal on earth.

Chimpanzees can recognize their own image in a mirror.

Cats can sleep up to 16 hours a day.

A fox is related to a dog.

Maze Mystery

Help the lambs meet their friends, Romeo and Mallowpuff, by finding a way out of the maze.

Start

Finish

Answers on page 69

Quiz Whizz!

1. How many legs does a spider have?
   a. 4
   b. 6
   c. 8

2. Where does a bird live?
   a. A nest
   b. A burrow
   c. A house

3. How many tentacles does an octopus have?
   a. 2
   b. 6
   c. 8

4. Which of these animals is black and white?
   a. A panda
   b. A koala bear
   c. A fox

5. Which of these animals has horns?
   a. A rhinoceros
   b. A donkey
   c. A squirrel

6. What noise does a frog make?
   a. Squeak
   b. Oink
   c. Croak

Maggie

Romeo

King Geoffrey

Answers on page 69

You will need:

Two pieces of card
Scissors
Glue
Glitter
Photographs, or
Pictures of animals
Sticky tack

Misty

1. Cut two pieces of card 15cm (6 inches) x 20cm (8 inches)
2. Draw a 3cm (1.25 inches) border inside one piece of card, as shown in picture a. Ask an adult to cut this out. The border will become your frame.
3. Add spots and patterns, with the glue, around the frame. Sprinkle with glitter and sequins and leave to dry.
4. On the other piece of card, stick a picture of your animal.
5. Once dry, shake the excess glitter off your frame. Glue the frame on top of your animal picture, as shown in picture b.
6. Use sticky tack to hang it on your bedroom wall for everyone to see.

a

b

Rosette

King Arthur

You will need:

Two pieces of card
Crepe paper
Scissors
Ribbon
A pen
Glue

King Arthur

1. Cut two identical circles from the card.
2. Cut a long strip of crepe paper 3.5cm (1.5 inches) wide — you can always attach two strips together if it is not long enough.
3. Glue one end of the crepe paper to the edge of one of the circles. You should fold the crepe paper and follow the edge of the circle, gluing the crepe paper down, as shown in picture a.
4. Glue the two pieces of ribbon at the bottom of the circle, on top of the crepe paper, as shown in picture b.
5. Now stick the second circle on top so that the crepe paper is sandwiched between the two circles of card.
6. Write a message on the top piece of card and use it as a prize for your pet.

a

b

Best Pet

Decorate Me

Decorate this picture in any way you like.
You could even add some stickers.

Find the Pair

Can you spot which picture only appears twice?

Odd One Out

Which of these pictures of Mango is the odd one out?
What is different about it?

a   b   c

Answers on page 69

Harry

Harry loves to spend summer days making daisy chains.

My birthday: 2nd February

I like: playing games

I don't like: the cold

One word that describes me is: bouncy

My perfect day: bouncing in the flowerbeds

The food I like best: flower petals

The place I like best: the greenhouse

What I would like to be when I'm older: a florist

My best toy: a squeaky carrot

Lacey

Lacey loves cooking cupcakes with frosting on top.

My birthday: 14th July

I like: playing hide-and-seek

I don't like: lots of noise

One word that describes me is: shy

My perfect day: baking delicious cakes

The food I like best: cream cakes

The place I like best: the kitchen

What I would like to be when I'm older: a chef

My best toy: a bouncy ball

Bunny School

It's another busy day at bunny school and there's lots of lessons today.

Troy

Storytime

"Come on everyone, it's Nature Studies first. Let's see what we can find outside." says Troy.

"I'm looking in the tall grass," says Mr McGregor, smiling. "I can see lots of pretty white flowers. I wonder what else we'll find."

Mr McGregor

"Look! I've found a pretty butterfly!" shouts Mr Hopper, excitedly. "It has the most beautiful wings I've ever seen."

Mr Hopper

Primrose

"I've picked some daisies and made a daisy chain," Primrose says, happily. "The flowers smell nice and it makes a very pretty necklace."

Sage

"Now it's time for an Arts and Crafts lesson. Let's make things!" says Sage. "This is the best class of the day."

"Uh-oh! I think we've made a bit of a mess with this paint," laughs Parsley. "Look at our sticky, orange paw-prints all over the floor."

Parsley and Thyme

Ebony

"Look!" says Ebony. "I've made a red and white stripy scarf with tassles at the end. It will keep me nice and warm when it's cold outside."

It's nearly the end of the day.

"Finished at last, says Max. "I've made a woolly hat with a fluffy bobble on the top."

Briiiing! Briiing!

"That's the bell. School's Out."

Max

Kitty Collage

You will need:
Lots of different shades of paper
A piece of white card
Scissors
Glue
A pencil

Tiger Lily

1. Using a pencil, draw a picture of a kitten onto a large piece of white card.

2. Tear up lots of different shades of paper into small pieces (you could even use old magazines).

a

3. Use these pieces to create your kitten picture by gluing them into the outline of your pet, as shown in picture a.

4. You can create a collage of anything. Try making a collage of a different animal.

5. Use your pictures to decorate your bedroom.

Pin the Tail on the Pony

You will need:

A large piece
of white paper
Lots of different
shades of paper
Scissors
Sticky tack
Pens or crayons

Precious

1. Draw a picture of a pony, without a tail, onto your piece of white paper. Decorate it and stick the picture of the pony onto a wall, or the back of a door, using the sticky tack.

2. To play 'pin the tail on the pony' you will need two or more players. Each player should draw a tail onto a different shade of paper. They should then use a pen to write their name on their tail. Ask an adult to cut the tails out.

3. Stick a piece of sticky tack to the back of each tail.

4. Take it in turns with your friends and family to play 'pin the tail on the pony'.

5. One person should close their eyes, holding the horse's tail with their name on it. Another person should spin them round once and then lead them to the picture of the horse. The game is trying to pin the tail on the pony in the right place with your eyes closed. The person nearest wins!

Top Tip! If you don't have a piece of white paper big enough, you can tape four smaller pieces together instead.

Hoppity-Hop

You will need a friend to play with.
Each of you will need to use a coin for a counter.
You will also need a dice.

Start
1

2

3

12

11

10

13

14

15

24

23

22

25

26

27

1. Each player chooses a sticker from the sticker sheet and sticks it to a coin. Put your coins on the start space.
2. Take turns to roll the dice.
3. If you land on a space with a bunny, move forward two spaces. If you land on a space with a guinea pig, you must move back three spaces.
4. The first one to reach the finish wins!

4

5

6

9

8

7

16

17

18

21

20

19

28

29

Finish

30

47

Spot the Difference

Devon just loves to play hide-and-seek!
Can you find the five differences between
these two pictures?

Odd One Out

Which of these is a noise that a dog doesn't make? b

a Woof

b Oink

c Bark

d Howl

48

Answers on page 69

Quiz Whizz!

1. Where does a seahorse live?
   a.   In the sea ✓
   b.   In the jungle
   c.   On the farm

2. What animal can change colour?
   a.   A badger
   b.   A chameleon ✓
   c.   A tortoise

3. Which animal doesn't have a tail?
   a.   A gorilla ✓
   b.   A fish
   c.   A kitten

4. What animal doesn't have its
   home on its back?
   a.   A tortoise
   b.   A snail
   c.   A bunny ✓

5. Which of these animals has
   hooves?
   a.   A snake
   b.   A horse ✓
   c.   A monkey

6. Which one of these animals howl?
   a.   A wolf ✓
   b.   A giraffe
   c.   A pony

Answers on page 69

Penelope

Precious

Manyara

How to make an... Animal Door Hanger

You will need:
Card
Tracing paper
Scissors
Pens
Glue

1. Trace the shape below onto the card and ask an adult to cut it out for you.
2. Fold the door hanger shape in half and stick the back sides together.
3. Draw a picture of a sleeping animal on one side and write 'Do Not Disturb' with your pens.
4. On the other side, draw a picture of an animal playing with its toys and write 'Come In.'
5. Decorate it any way you like.
6. Now hang it on your bedroom door.

Fold here

Do Not Disturb

Come In

Animal Scrapbook

Poppy

You will need:

Two pieces of
pink card
10-15 sheets
of white paper
A hole punch
A piece of ribbon
2 Beads (optional)
Glue

1. Take your sheets of white paper, then put one piece of pink card on the top and one on the bottom of the stack.

2. Make sure all pages are lined up and ask an adult to make holes with a hole punch all the way down the long edge.

3. Thread the ribbon through the holes and tie a knot at both ends so it does not become loose. You could even thread on some beads.

4. To decorate the front of your book, you could stick pictures of animals, draw paw prints, or even stick on leaves and feathers you have found outside in your garden.

5. Use this book to write lots of special things about the animals you love.

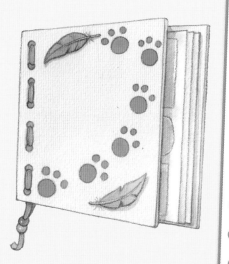

Puzzles

Wrong Way

Which path of paw prints will lead Tarquin
to his yummy dinner?

a

b

c

Odd One Out

Which of these pictures is the odd one out? a
What is different about it? different coloured spots

a

b

c

52

Answers on page 69

Draw the Perfect Picture

Draw a picture of you and your pet,
or an animal that you wish you had as a pet.
Add some stickers to your picture.

Lolly

Lolly loves to style her hair with pretty hairbands.

My birthday: 17th June

I like: laughing

I don't like: being sad

One word that describes me is: funny

My perfect day: telling jokes and making my friends laugh

The food I like best: juicy bones

The place I like best: on the sofa

What I would like to be when I'm older: an actor

My best toy: a bouncy ball

Kobi

Kobi is full of adventure and loves to discover new things.

My birthday: 5th October

I like: discovering new places and getting into trouble

I don't like: staying inside

One word that describes me is: adventurous

My perfect day: chasing butterflies in the garden

The food I like best: fishy treats

The place I like best: playing by the pond

What I would like to be when I'm older: a detective

My best toy: a cardboard tube

Pony Party

It's Enchanted's birthday today
and everyone is getting ready for her
big birthday party.

Fancy

"I can't wait,"
says Fancy,
"this party will be so
much fun!
I think I'll wear these
pretty pink flowers."

"Although, maybe
these sweet-smelling
yellow ones are better?"
she says.
"Yes, I think these
ones are best."

"I don't know what to wear," says Maggie. "Perhaps I should wear my pink fairy wings?"

Maggie

"Or maybe my special sparkly cowboy hat? I just can't decide which looks best!" she laughs.

Abby

"I wonder if I should wear these pretty flowers in my mane?" says Abby.

"Or perhaps it would look better if I wore some beautiful flowers around my neck?" she says.

"I know what I'm going to wear," smiles Prancer. "My best pink hat, of course!"

Prancer

It's time for the party!

Enchanted

"Come on everyone, let's go!" shouts Enchanted. "This is going to be the best party ever!"

Bird in a Cage

You will need:

Thick white card
Pens
String
Scissors

Prince

1. Ask an adult to cut a circle from the card.

2. Draw a picture of a bird on one side. Then draw a birdcage upside down on the reverse side of the circle, as shown in picture a.

3. Ask an adult to make a hole on either side of the disc.

4. Cut two pieces of string 40cm (16 inches) long and tie one to each side of the circle.

5. Hold one piece of string in each hand and spin the disc over and over, so that the string is twisted.

6. Then pull the pieces of string and watch the disc spin, as shown in picture b. The bird will look like it's in a cage.

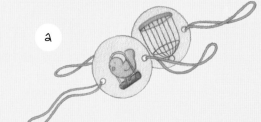

a

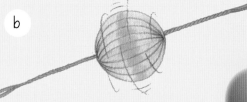

b

Pretty Pegs

You will need:
Clothes pegs
Glue
Paint
Paintbrush
Ribbon or string
Card
Pens
Sticky tack

1. Paint some pegs in any shade you like and leave them to dry.
2. Draw animals onto lots of different shades of card. Ask an adult to cut them out for you.
3. Decorate each animal with your pens.
4. Glue each animal onto the long flat side of a clothes peg.
5. Hang a piece of ribbon, or string, up in your bedroom using the sticky tack.
6. Clip the pegs on the ribbon to hang up your best photos and drawings.

Did you know...

The eyesight and hearing of dogs are better than that of humans.

A crocodile can never stick its tongue out.

An elephant cannot jump

A duck-billed platypus is the only mammal to lay eggs.

A woodpecker can peck up to 20 times every second.

A hedgehog's heart beats approximately 300 times a minute.

A snail can sleep for up to three years.

On average, a hen can lay between 228 and 350 eggs in a year.

No two zebras have the same striped pattern.

A giraffe uses its tongue to clean its own ears.

A donkey can see all four feet at the same time.

Goldfish can live for up to 10 years.

A chameleon can move its eyes in two different directions at the same time.

A cat uses its whiskers to decide if a space is too small to get through.

Apes are the most intelligent animals after humans.

A cow gives between 200,000 and 350,000 glasses of milk in her lifetime.

Join the Dots

Join the dots to find out what animal Bonnie is,
then have fun decorating her.

Spot the Pieces

Can you spot which pieces complete the puzzle?

a

b

c

d

Opposites

Draw lines to match the pictures to their opposites!

Awake

Small

Black

White

Asleep

Big

65

Answers on page 69

Birdfeeder

You will need:
String
Scissors
A plastic party plate
Peanuts, or seeds
Paint
PVA glue
A paintbrush

Henny and Penny

1. Mix your paint with the PVA glue (you should mix 3/4 paint and 1/4 glue) and then decorate your plastic plate. Leave to dry.

2. Cut three pieces of string approximately 30cm (12 inches) long.

3. Ask an adult to make three holes, evenly spaced around the outside of the plastic plate.

4. Tie a knot in the end of one piece of string and thread a bead onto it. Then thread your piece of string through one of the holes on the underside of the plate.

5. Do this for the other two pieces of string and the other two holes.

6. Tie all three pieces of string together in a knot at the top. Hang over a branch of a tree in your garden.

7. Fill the plate with peanuts and seeds and watch the birds.

Pencil Topper

1. Fold the card in half and draw a picture of the animal you like most onto it.

2. Decorate it using pens and crayons.

3. Ask an adult to cut out the animal, keeping the card folded. You should now have a piece of card for the front of your animal, and a piece of card for the back of your animal.

4. Sandwich the pipe cleaner between the pieces of card and glue in place.

5. Wind the pipe cleaner around one of your best pencils and you have made your very own pencil topper.

You will need:

White card
Pens
Glue
A pencil

Handprint Butterfly

1. Draw a picture of a butterfly's body onto the piece of white card and use your pens to decorate it.

2. Paint your hand with poster paint and make four handprints around the butterfly's body, as shown in the picture.

3. Try making some different butterflies, some could have purple wings, some could have blue wings and some can have both! You could even use your paintbrush to add patterns to the butterflies' wings.

You will need:

White card
Scissors
Paint
Glue
A paintbrush

Jokes

Why do cows lie down when it rains?

To keep each udder dry!

What's black, white and red all over?

A penguin with sunburn!

What do you get when you cross a cat and a parrot?

A carrot!

What's striped and bounces up and down?

A tiger on a pogo stick!

Where would you take a poorly horse?

The horse-pital!

What did the farmer give to the sick chicken?

Tweetment!

What do you call a dancing sheep?

A baaaaa-llerina!

ANSWERS

Page 12: SPOT THE DIFFERENCE
Picture b: One cat has a red nose, one cat has blue eyes, there is a blue flower on the right box, the pink flower has a green center, and there is a green flower on the top box.

Page 12: CLOSE UP
a=2, b=3, c=1

Page 13: ODD ONE OUT
Picture c - all of the other pictures are dogs.

Page 13: SILHOUETTE MATCH
Picture b is the silhouette of Maddie.

Page 18: QUIZ WHIZZ! 1
1=b, 2=a, 3=c, 4=b, 5=b, 6=b

Page 19: COUNTING FUN
a+c, b+f, d+e

Page 20: WHO EATS WHAT?
a=3, b=2, c=1

Page 20: REMEMBER ME
1= there were 9 pockets, 2= 4 black cats, 3 = 2 pockets had bows on them

Page 21: MISSING PIECES
1=b, 2=c, 3=a

Page 21: WHICH WAY
Line b leads Malaika and Malai to their basket.

Page 32: MAZE MYSTERY

Page 33: QUIZ WHIZZ! 2
1=c, 2=a, 3=c, 4=a, 5=a, 6=c

Page 37: FIND THE PAIR
The bunny only appears twice

Page 37: ODD ONE OUT
Picture b. The sprinkles on the cupcake are all pink.

Page 48: SPOT THE DIFFERENCE
Picture b: Devon has a blue nose, there is a paw print on the left of the bag, one flower on the bag is blue, there is an extra purple pawrint on the bag and there is an extra green flower on the bag.

Page 48: ODD ONE OUT
A dog doesn't oink (b).

Page 49: QUIZ WHIZZ! 3
1=a, 2=b, 3=a, 4=c, 5=b, 6=a

Page 52: WRONG WAY
Line a leadsTarquin to his dinner.

Page 52: ODD ONE OUT
Picture a. The dots are pink on the bow.

Page 64: JOIN THE DOTS
Bonnie is a dog.

Page 65: SPOT THE PIECES
Pieces a and b complete the puzzle.

Page 65: OPPOSTIES
Awake = Asleep, Small = Big, White = Black

Zsa Zsa

Buffy

Patches

Liam

Angelo

Prancer